My First Owl Book

By Carrie Casey

Thank you so much for purchasing this eBook! We had so much fun creating this book for you to enjoy. We trust you will have as much fun reading it as we did creating it.

If you like this story, we'd be most grateful if you'd help us out by taking a few moments and leaving us a review on Amazon. Thank you so much!

As a FREE BONUS for purchasing this eBook, for a limited time, we'd like to gift you an owl activity pack for you and your loved ones to add your own color and creativity to. Go to https://tinyurl.com/53ay7pv2 to get your packet.

Peace, love, and hoots,
Carrie and Joanna Casey

Published by CEY Press
821 Grand Ave, Suite 119
Pflugerville, TX 78660

Copyright © 2021 by Carrie Casey
My First Owl Book: A Rhyming Animal Book for Young Children

edited by Joanna Casey

ISBN:

Text copyright © 2021   by Carrie Casey
Illustrations provided by Ahmed Badawy, Richard Lee, Stephen Penderson, Cliff Johnson, Pete Nuij, Robin Canfield, Manidep Mandal, Taleon Pinherio, Zdenek Machacek, Ansie Potgieler, Gary Bendig, James Beekers & AJ Jean

My First Owl Book

By Carrie Casey

OWLS TAKE FLIGHT AT NIGHT.

THEY FLY THROUGH THE SKY.

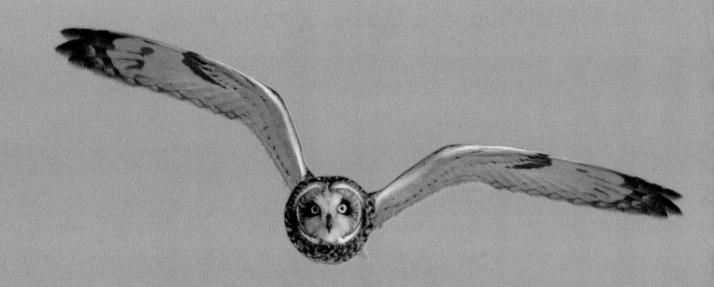

THEY LIKE TO HIDE.

SOME HIDE

INSIDE.

SOME HIDE

OUTSIDE.

SOME HIDE IN THE SNOW.

SOME ARE FOUND ON THE GROUND.

THESE 3 ARE

IN A TREE.

THESE 3 PICKED A POST.

THIS ONE PERCHED ON A CHURCH.

BUT OWLS LIKE A NEST THE MOST.

IN A TREE, ON THE GROUND, OR IN THE AIR OWLS ARE AMAZING!

Made in the USA
Las Vegas, NV
09 January 2023

65339278R00017